ANSWERS

Pages 8–9

Page 13

Page 17

Page 21

1) Zebra

2) Giraffe

3) Hippo

Published by RBA Coleccionables, S.A.U.
Av. Diagonal, 189 – 08018 Barcelona, Spain. ESA-78898350

© 2018 RBA Coleccionables, S.A.U.

My Zoo Animals
Produced by Editec
English adaptation by Vespa Design

Book design: IMC

Text: Elisabet Benet, Caterina López i Rigo, Gemma Sanz, Oriol Parreño

Illustrations & Layout: Tenllado Studio and Esteban Gómez Ilustración

Illustrators: Marc Alberich and Alexis Capera

ISSN: 2057-4240

Printed in Spain

It's easy to continue your collection:

To receive your issues by post, or if you missed an issue, call Customer Services or visit the website:

UK and Ireland ... 0344 472 5240   **www.myzooanimals.co.uk**

LUMBA
THE LION

MY ZOO ANIMALS

RBA

LUMBA'S PRIDE

Welcome to the zoo! This is the zoo's pride of lions: a very big, strong lion called Lumba, two lionesses and some very mischievous cubs.

You can see Lumba the lion lying on top of that rock, keeping watch over his pride. He's the boss!

The lions live in a very big enclosure with trees and rocks. Visitors can't go in because the lions can be quite ferocious.

GRRR!

Sometimes the lion roars. It's so loud that it scares all the other animals and you can even hear it outside the zoo!

WHAT DO I LOOK LIKE?

I'm Lumba the lion, the bravest animal in the zoo. All of the other animals respect me. I'm the king!

SMALL EARS

BIG BROWN EYES

LONG SHARP TEETH

AGE: LIVES AROUND 25 YEARS.

HEIGHT: 1 METRE TALL.

WEIGHT: 200KG – AS HEAVY AS YOU AND 10 OF YOUR CLASSMATES ALL TOGETHER!

PAWS WITH VERY SHARP CLAWS

A TYPICAL DAY

MORNING

I wake up early when it's cooler and the zoo hasn't opened yet. I play with the cubs for a while. They never get tired! They're always calling out to me, "You can't catch us, Lumba!"

ALWAYS SLEEPY!

Lions can sleep up to twenty hours each day. How many hours do you sleep?

AFTERNOON

After so much activity, I like to lie down and have a nap. I'm so sleepy! I spend hours resting on my comfy rock and keeping a watchful eye over the pride.

NIGHT

At night, when it gets dark, we eat dinner together, but there is a pecking order. I eat first, then the lionesses and the cubs. We love meat. We are carnivores!

THE STAR OF THE ZOO

All the boys and girls who visit the zoo come and see the lions. They want to see the little cubs playing, but most of all they want to see me, the king! I'm the star of the zoo! They can see that the lionesses are smaller and don't have a magnificent mane like mine.

They know me and they call out to me. Sometimes they shout, "Lumba, wake up!" I pretend I can't hear them and carry on sleeping. But sometimes I lift my head, look at them angrily and give a loud roar, showing them my big teeth. Some of them scream. It's great fun!

OOPS!

Three of the people in the picture are wearing the wrong type of clothes for a sunny day at the zoo. Can you find them?

MY NEIGHBOURS

I have lots of friends in the zoo.
They all live in their own special areas.

The friend I see the most is Sandy the giraffe. She has a very long neck so her head peeps out above the trees and she tells me everything that's going on.

I also know the elephants. They say hello with their trunks while they're having a bath. They always have lots of fun, but can be very noisy.

The tigers are like my cousins. We look very similar, but their fur is orange with black stripes. They roar like me too and some of the visitors get scared.

My friend Lolo the hippopotamus lives in a big swimming pool. He's always in the water. Lolo is very serious and doesn't even laugh at my jokes!

THEY'RE ALWAYS LAUGHING!

In the zoo, as well as the roars of the lions and tigers, you can hear a little laughter. It's the hyenas; they're always happy.

Hee hee hee!

WE'VE HAD SOME LION CUBS!

Surprise! Some lion cubs were born in Lumba's pride last night. They're very small and look just like kittens. They can't even walk or open their eyes to see anything yet.

I've taken them to the animal hospital to weigh and measure them and give them some milk. They were really hungry!

12

After a few weeks, the cubs have grown. They've learned to walk and want to play all the time. Now I can leave them with the rest of the lions.

The whole pride is very happy. The lionesses share the work of looking after them, cleaning them with their tongues and feeding them milk. The little cubs run around all day. Don't they look cute!

WHAT A MESS!

The cubs have made a real mess in the animal hospital! They're very naughty! Follow the wool threads to find out which colour each cub has chosen.

A CHECK-UP WITH THE VET

Charles the vet

Once a year, I visit Lumba to check him over and make sure he's doing well. However lions are very ferocious, so I need to put him to sleep before I can examine him.

Once he's asleep, I take him to the zoo hospital where I can brush his teeth, especially his long canines and his smaller incisors which he uses to tear the meat he eats every day.

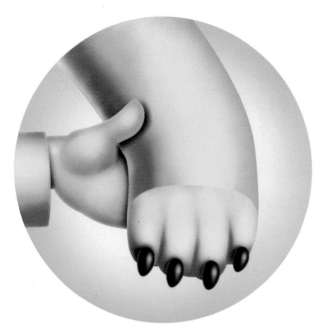

While he's asleep, I check that his paws are all right and look for any injuries that might have occurred.

I weigh him to make sure he hasn't put on or lost weight. He's the king of the zoo and he needs to be strong and healthy.

SHARP CLAWS!

Lumba's paws have very sharp claws that he uses to climb trees. Charles the vet cuts his claws once a year. You cut your nails too, don't you?

HAPPY BIRTHDAY!

The day Lumba was born.

Lumba when he was 3.

Today's a great day! I arrived at the zoo about six years ago.
I was only seven months old. All the lions spoiled me and licked me
and they didn't mind when I was a bit mischievous.
After a while, I grew a mane and got bigger and stronger.
Look how much I've changed!

I'm really happy because the zoo is throwing a birthday party for me. They've hung up bunting and balloons. A clown is telling the boys and girls about lions, and they're laughing and clapping. My present? A really big steak! Yum, it's delicious!

HIDE AND SEEK

There are three animals hiding at Lumba's party. Can you find them? Here are their shadows to help you.

LIONS AND FELINES

Lions are in the family of cats called felines, like pet cats, but wilder... and so much bigger! Felines sneak around and are very quiet hunters.

THERE ARE TWO LARGE GROUPS OF LIONS:

AFRICAN LIONS

LIKE LUMBA, THEY ARE STRONGER AND THEIR MANES ARE LONGER AND THICKER.

ASIATIC LIONS

THEY ARE SMALLER THAN AFRICAN LIONS. THEY HAVE SHORTER MANES AND NARROWER MUZZLES.

THERE ARE OTHER WILD FELINES TOO

TIGERS
THE LARGEST FELINES. THEIR FUR HAS BLACK STRIPES.

LEOPARDS
THEIR FUR HAS BLACK SPOTS. WHEN THEIR FUR IS BLACK THEY ARE CALLED PANTHERS.

CHEETAHS
THEIR FUR IS SPOTTED. THEY ARE THE FASTEST LAND ANIMALS IN THE WORLD.

SERVALS
THE SMALLEST OF THE FELINES. THEY EAT RODENTS.

WHERE DO WE LIVE?

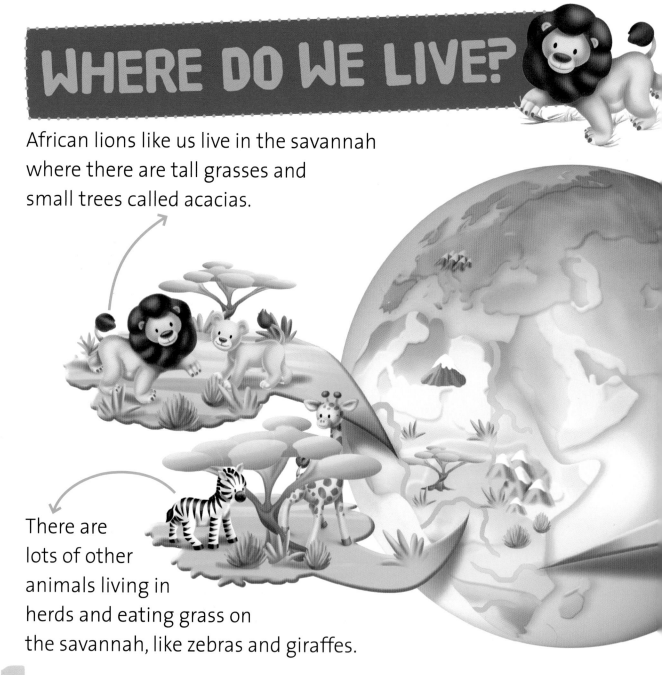

African lions like us live in the savannah where there are tall grasses and small trees called acacias.

There are lots of other animals living in herds and eating grass on the savannah, like zebras and giraffes.

The Asiatic lions live in a forest in India. There are very few left and they live in an area where they are protected called a 'reserve'.

Crocodiles and hippopotamuses live in the rivers.

THE STORY OF

MENGO
THE NEW KING
OF THE SAVANNAH

Mengo was a three-year-old lion who had grown a lot. He had a twin sister called Panga. Mengo had to leave his pride because he was all grown up; but because she was a lioness, Panga could stay with her family. "Why do I have to go?" asked Mengo. "I'm very happy here with you."

"This is how lions do things. You have to find your pride on the savannah," said his mother, with tears in her eyes.

Mengo was very sad as he went off towards the faraway plains. One night, he reached a river and climbed up onto a tree branch to rest. Suddenly, he heard an animal that was laughing. It was Lunta, the hyena, talking to herself. Even though she was laughing, she was sad. "The same thing always happens to me," said Lunta. "When I tell the giraffes or the gnus something, they don't believe me. I keep laughing and they don't take me seriously. They get angry and leave because they think I'm teasing them. And here I am, alone on the savannah!"

"Hyena, try not to laugh and cry at the same time. Tomorrow I'll help you make friends," said Mengo from the branch. He was careful not to roar because he didn't want to scare her.

"You? A fierce lion all alone? I don't know if I can trust you," she answered, laughing.

"Trust me, you'll make friends. But in return, because you know this area well, you must introduce me to a pride of lions I can live with," said the lion.

"All right, I'll take you to Acacia Plain where there's a group of lionesses without a lion to protect them," Lunta promised. In the morning, they went to see the giraffes, the gazelles and the gnus.

"Let me introduce my friend the lion," Lunta said to them. They didn't believe her, as usual. How could a hyena and a lion be friends?

But then Mengo appeared and they realised it was true.
"All right!" they said when they saw him, "We'll be your friends."
"Now I'm really laughing," cried Lunta, when she saw how scared
the animals were as they looked at Mengo. "Ha ha ha!"
Afterwards, Lunta took Mengo to Acacia Plain, where there was a
group of lionesses. When they reached them, she said, " Lionesses,
let me introduce Mengo, the bravest, most handsome lion on the
savannah. He could be the new leader of your pride. He will hunt
with you and protect you."
And that's what happened. Mengo became a strong lion with a big
mane. Every night, in Acacia Plain, he roared. Although she was very
far away, his sister Panga could hear him and would reply, "Good
night, Mengo!"